2022
HOMEMAKER'S FRIEND

daily
PLANNER

The 2022 Homemaker's Friend
Daily Planner is dedicated to
LANETTE STEINER.
First colleagues and now friends.
I love how God merged
our paths, placed us in
the same community
and occasionally in the
same coffee shop.

sue hooley

2022 DAILY PLANNER

Christian Light Publications, Inc.
Harrisonburg, Virginia 22802

©2021 Christian Light Publications, Inc.
All rights reserved.
Printed in China.

ISBN: 978-0-87813-272-0

To order planners by mail, please use order form in back.
Your comments and suggestions are welcomed!

Cover Design: Lanette Steiner
Text Design: Rhoda Miller & Lanette Steiner

A SPECIAL NOTE OF THANKS
TO KATHERINE DERSTINE

for choosing the Scripture verses. The verses contain the theme of
JOURNEYING IN FAITH AND TRUST.

We know God is safe to trust, but when the future is uncertain, it takes faith to totally trust God. Keep walking. God is waiting for you around the curve in the road. He has promised, "I am continually with thee: thou hast holden me by my right hand." Psalm 73:23.

THIS **DAILY PLANNER** BELONGS TO:

_____

_____

_____

_____

_____

IMPORTANT PHONE NUMBERS:

NAME   PHONE

_____   _____

_____   _____

_____   _____

_____   _____

_____   _____

_____   _____

_____   _____

_____   _____

_____   _____

_____   _____

IF THE PLAN DOESN'T WORK, CHANGE THE PLAN BUT NEVER THE GOAL.

TWO THOUSAND TWENTY-ONE

JANUARY 2021

S	M	T	W	T	F	S
					1	2
3	4	5	6	7	8	9
10	11	12	13	14	15	16
17	18	19	20	21	22	23
24	25	26	27	28	29	30
31						

FEBRUARY 2021

S	M	T	W	T	F	S
	1	2	3	4	5	6
7	8	9	10	11	12	13
14	15	16	17	18	19	20
21	22	23	24	25	26	27
28						

MARCH 2021

S	M	T	W	T	F	S
	1	2	3	4	5	6
7	8	9	10	11	12	13
14	15	16	17	18	19	20
21	22	23	24	25	26	27
28	29	30	31			

APRIL 2021

S	M	T	W	T	F	S
				1	2	3
4	5	6	7	8	9	10
11	12	13	14	15	16	17
18	19	20	21	22	23	24
25	26	27	28	29	30	

MAY 2021

S	M	T	W	T	F	S
						1
2	3	4	5	6	7	8
9	10	11	12	13	14	15
16	17	18	19	20	21	22
23	24	25	26	27	28	29
30	31					

JUNE 2021

S	M	T	W	T	F	S
		1	2	3	4	5
6	7	8	9	10	11	12
13	14	15	16	17	18	19
20	21	22	23	24	25	26
27	28	29	30			

JULY 2021

S	M	T	W	T	F	S
				1	2	3
4	5	6	7	8	9	10
11	12	13	14	15	16	17
18	19	20	21	22	23	24
25	26	27	28	29	30	31

AUGUST 2021

S	M	T	W	T	F	S
1	2	3	4	5	6	7
8	9	10	11	12	13	14
15	16	17	18	19	20	21
22	23	24	25	26	27	28
29	30	31				

SEPTEMBER 2021

S	M	T	W	T	F	S
			1	2	3	4
5	6	7	8	9	10	11
12	13	14	15	16	17	18
19	20	21	22	23	24	25
26	27	28	29	30		

OCTOBER 2021

S	M	T	W	T	F	S
					1	2
3	4	5	6	7	8	9
10	11	12	13	14	15	16
17	18	19	20	21	22	23
24	25	26	27	28	29	30
31						

NOVEMBER 2021

S	M	T	W	T	F	S
	1	2	3	4	5	6
7	8	9	10	11	12	13
14	15	16	17	18	19	20
21	22	23	24	25	26	27
28	29	30				

DECEMBER 2021

S	M	T	W	T	F	S
			1	2	3	4
5	6	7	8	9	10	11
12	13	14	15	16	17	18
19	20	21	22	23	24	25
26	27	28	29	30	31	

TWO THOUSAND TWENTY-TWO

JANUARY 2022

S	M	T	W	T	F	S
						1
2	3	4	5	6	7	8
9	10	11	12	13	14	15
16	17	18	19	20	21	22
23	24	25	26	27	28	29
30	31					

FEBRUARY 2022

S	M	T	W	T	F	S
		1	2	3	4	5
6	7	8	9	10	11	12
13	14	15	16	17	18	19
20	21	22	23	24	25	26
27	28					

MARCH 2022

S	M	T	W	T	F	S
		1	2	3	4	5
6	7	8	9	10	11	12
13	14	15	16	17	18	19
20	21	22	23	24	25	26
27	28	29	30	31		

APRIL 2022

S	M	T	W	T	F	S
					1	2
3	4	5	6	7	8	9
10	11	12	13	14	15	16
17	18	19	20	21	22	23
24	25	26	27	28	29	30

MAY 2022

S	M	T	W	T	F	S
1	2	3	4	5	6	7
8	9	10	11	12	13	14
15	16	17	18	19	20	21
22	23	24	25	26	27	28
29	30	31				

JUNE 2022

S	M	T	W	T	F	S
			1	2	3	4
5	6	7	8	9	10	11
12	13	14	15	16	17	18
19	20	21	22	23	24	25
26	27	28	29	30		

JULY 2022

S	M	T	W	T	F	S
					1	2
3	4	5	6	7	8	9
10	11	12	13	14	15	16
17	18	19	20	21	22	23
24	25	26	27	28	29	30
31						

AUGUST 2022

S	M	T	W	T	F	S
	1	2	3	4	5	6
7	8	9	10	11	12	13
14	15	16	17	18	19	20
21	22	23	24	25	26	27
28	29	30	31			

SEPTEMBER 2022

S	M	T	W	T	F	S
				1	2	3
4	5	6	7	8	9	10
11	12	13	14	15	16	17
18	19	20	21	22	23	24
25	26	27	28	29	30	

OCTOBER 2022

S	M	T	W	T	F	S
						1
2	3	4	5	6	7	8
9	10	11	12	13	14	15
16	17	18	19	20	21	22
23	24	25	26	27	28	29
30	31					

NOVEMBER 2022

S	M	T	W	T	F	S
		1	2	3	4	5
6	7	8	9	10	11	12
13	14	15	16	17	18	19
20	21	22	23	24	25	26
27	28	29	30			

DECEMBER 2022

S	M	T	W	T	F	S
				1	2	3
4	5	6	7	8	9	10
11	12	13	14	15	16	17
18	19	20	21	22	23	24
25	26	27	28	29	30	31

TWO THOUSAND TWENTY-THREE

JANUARY 2023

S	M	T	W	T	F	S
1	2	3	4	5	6	7
8	9	10	11	12	13	14
15	16	17	18	19	20	21
22	23	24	25	26	27	28
29	30	31				

FEBRUARY 2023

S	M	T	W	T	F	S
			1	2	3	4
5	6	7	8	9	10	11
12	13	14	15	16	17	18
19	20	21	22	23	24	25
26	27	28				

MARCH 2023

S	M	T	W	T	F	S
			1	2	3	4
5	6	7	8	9	10	11
12	13	14	15	16	17	18
19	20	21	22	23	24	25
26	27	28	29	30	31	

APRIL 2023

S	M	T	W	T	F	S
						1
2	3	4	5	6	7	8
9	10	11	12	13	14	15
16	17	18	19	20	21	22
23	24	25	26	27	28	29
30						

MAY 2023

S	M	T	W	T	F	S
	1	2	3	4	5	6
7	8	9	10	11	12	13
14	15	16	17	18	19	20
21	22	23	24	25	26	27
28	29	30	31			

JUNE 2023

S	M	T	W	T	F	S
				1	2	3
4	5	6	7	8	9	10
11	12	13	14	15	16	17
18	19	20	21	22	23	24
25	26	27	28	29	30	

JULY 2023

S	M	T	W	T	F	S
						1
2	3	4	5	6	7	8
9	10	11	12	13	14	15
16	17	18	19	20	21	22
23	24	25	26	27	28	29
30	31					

AUGUST 2023

S	M	T	W	T	F	S
		1	2	3	4	5
6	7	8	9	10	11	12
13	14	15	16	17	18	19
20	21	22	23	24	25	26
27	28	29	30	31		

SEPTEMBER 2023

S	M	T	W	T	F	S
					1	2
3	4	5	6	7	8	9
10	11	12	13	14	15	16
17	18	19	20	21	22	23
24	25	26	27	28	29	30

OCTOBER 2023

S	M	T	W	T	F	S
1	2	3	4	5	6	7
8	9	10	11	12	13	14
15	16	17	18	19	20	21
22	23	24	25	26	27	28
29	30	31				

NOVEMBER 2023

S	M	T	W	T	F	S
			1	2	3	4
5	6	7	8	9	10	11
12	13	14	15	16	17	18
19	20	21	22	23	24	25
26	27	28	29	30		

DECEMBER 2023

S	M	T	W	T	F	S
					1	2
3	4	5	6	7	8	9
10	11	12	13	14	15	16
17	18	19	20	21	22	23
24	25	26	27	28	29	30
31						

TWO THOUSAND TWENTY-FOUR

JANUARY 2024

S	M	T	W	T	F	S
	1	2	3	4	5	6
7	8	9	10	11	12	13
14	15	16	17	18	19	20
21	22	23	24	25	26	27
28	29	30	31			

FEBRUARY 2024

S	M	T	W	T	F	S
				1	2	3
4	5	6	7	8	9	10
11	12	13	14	15	16	17
18	19	20	21	22	23	24
25	26	27	28	29		

MARCH 2024

S	M	T	W	T	F	S
					1	2
3	4	5	6	7	8	9
10	11	12	13	14	15	16
17	18	19	20	21	22	23
24	25	26	27	28	29	30
31						

APRIL 2024

S	M	T	W	T	F	S
	1	2	3	4	5	6
7	8	9	10	11	12	13
14	15	16	17	18	19	20
21	22	23	24	25	26	27
28	29	30				

MAY 2024

S	M	T	W	T	F	S
			1	2	3	4
5	6	7	8	9	10	11
12	13	14	15	16	17	18
19	20	21	22	23	24	25
26	27	28	29	30	31	

JUNE 2024

S	M	T	W	T	F	S
						1
2	3	4	5	6	7	8
9	10	11	12	13	14	15
16	17	18	19	20	21	22
23	24	25	26	27	28	29
30						

JULY 2024

S	M	T	W	T	F	S
	1	2	3	4	5	6
7	8	9	10	11	12	13
14	15	16	17	18	19	20
21	22	23	24	25	26	27
28	29	30	31			

AUGUST 2024

S	M	T	W	T	F	S
				1	2	3
4	5	6	7	8	9	10
11	12	13	14	15	16	17
18	19	20	21	22	23	24
25	26	27	28	29	30	31

SEPTEMBER 2024

S	M	T	W	T	F	S
1	2	3	4	5	6	7
8	9	10	11	12	13	14
15	16	17	18	19	20	21
22	23	24	25	26	27	28
29	30					

OCTOBER 2024

S	M	T	W	T	F	S
		1	2	3	4	5
6	7	8	9	10	11	12
13	14	15	16	17	18	19
20	21	22	23	24	25	26
27	28	29	30	31		

NOVEMBER 2024

S	M	T	W	T	F	S
					1	2
3	4	5	6	7	8	9
10	11	12	13	14	15	16
17	18	19	20	21	22	23
24	25	26	27	28	29	30

DECEMBER 2024

S	M	T	W	T	F	S
1	2	3	4	5	6	7
8	9	10	11	12	13	14
15	16	17	18	19	20	21
22	23	24	25	26	27	28
29	30	31				

Hanging in Midair

The idiom "hanging in midair" creates a word picture that corresponds with our emotions about a situation. We know it is impossible to dangle in midair, but during times of uncertainty, that is exactly how we feel.

When we call out to God, we like when He leaps into action. One Sunday when our family came home from church, our daughter's prized golden retriever was missing. I felt heartsick and wondered how she would deal with losing another pet. After searching and calling for Ginger, I asked the Lord for a miracle and went to call the dog warden. I saw an unfamiliar number on the caller ID and immediately hit redial. "We have your dog," said a lady, without even waiting for a formal greeting.

But often in the weightier matters of life, answers do not come quickly. We pray. We wait. We pray some more. We know God has promised to meet our needs, but we continue to hang uncomfortably in midair.

Did King David occasionally feel that way too? He asked the following questions:

- "Why standest thou afar off, O LORD? why hidest thou thyself in times of trouble?" (Psalm 10:1).
- "How long wilt thou forget me, O LORD? for ever? how long wilt thou hide thy face from me?" (Psalm 13:1).
- "My God, my God, why hast thou forsaken me? why art thou so far from helping me, and from the words of my roaring?" (Psalm 22:1).

We can read the story of David's life in a matter of hours, and to us it is obvious that God was with him. Throughout the saga of his life, the Bible affirms that "the LORD was with him." Yet in some of his darkest moments, he asked questions like we do today.

In the verses above, David's questions and frustrations came in the first verse of the psalm. Then his words changed as he thought through issues and communed with the Lord.

- "The LORD is King for ever and ever" (Psalm 10:16).
- "But I have trusted in thy mercy; my heart shall rejoice in thy salvation. I will sing unto the LORD, because he hath dealt bountifully with me" (Psalm 13:5, 6).
- "For the kingdom is the LORD'S: and he is the governor among the nations" (Psalm 22:28).

David did not know how things would turn out in his life, but he chose to trust the Lord. We benefit from reading David's words of comfort, faith, and praise. Words that he wrote while "hanging in midair" give us reassurance today that the Lord is with us during difficult times.

We do not know how our lives will turn out. Sometimes the future feels uncertain, and worry invades our thoughts. A few years ago, Dan and I were facing a huge decision—one that we knew would impact our children's lives. As we discussed the matter, Dan often said, "The light doesn't shine that far on the path. As we move along, God will light up the way for us."

God does not ask us to figure out problems on our own. He asks us to trust Him and to recognize His sovereignty in our lives. Trusting God opens the way for us to base our security solely on Him and not on circumstances, other people, or our own thinking.

God knew the big picture for our family, and He faithfully led us. We "hung in midair" for months that turned into years. Then God lit up the path for us in a way we did not expect. As His plan unfolded, once again I realized that God is safe to trust. His presence went before us, paving our pathway so that He could guide our steps on an unfamiliar terrain.

God is in your story the same as He was in David's. He knows you and loves you. He is worthy of your trust and praise. If you are "hanging in midair," God understands. He has not forgotten you, and He is working in ways that you cannot see. Keep choosing trust. Let go of your worries and hold on to Him.

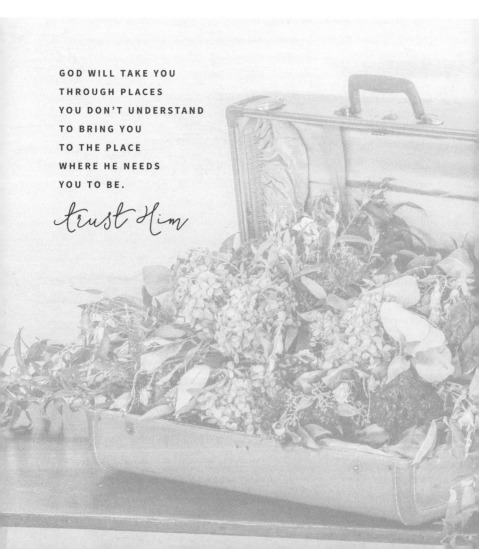

GOD WILL TAKE YOU
THROUGH PLACES
YOU DON'T UNDERSTAND
TO BRING YOU
TO THE PLACE
WHERE HE NEEDS
YOU TO BE.

trust Him

A B O U T *Sue*

The Daily Planner was designed by Sue Hooley, wife of Dan for 31 years and mother to six children, two girls and four boys ages 12-28. The planner was developed after several years of motherhood and homemaking. Sue understood that a homemaker's day can rarely be scheduled and structured the same as the one before, nor can every task fit neatly into the time slot allotted by other planners. Since her first publication in 2010, thousands of homemakers have benefited from the Daily Planner.

If you have comments about the Daily Planner, you may share your thoughts by sending an e-mail to: *office@homemakersdepot.com*
or writing to: Sue Hooley, 9849 Township Road 554, Holmesville, OH 44633
To read more, visit *www.homemakersdepot.com*

If you like this planner, help us out by leaving a review on Amazon.

TRY THESE MENU PLANNING WORKSHEETS AT NO RISK,

and . . .

- Make grocery shopping easier.
- Create balanced meals with more variety.
- Save money by planning in advance.
- Add flexibility to your meal schedule.
- Become more likely to try new recipes.
- Take advantage of sale items.

TO REQUEST YOUR
FREE PRINTABLE PDF,

send an e-mail to: *office@homemakersdepot.com*

or download it from our website at *www.homemakersdepot.com.*

THE FLEXIBLE PLANNER **FOR HOMEMAKERS**

Twenty years ago when I was a young homemaker, I read *Getting More Done in Less Time* by Donna Otto. She recommended using a simple daily planner to keep track of duties, appointments, and commitments. "It will be your friend for life," she promised.

I began my search for a planner that would help me organize my days and duties. But I soon realized that my homemaking days did not fit into neat little time slots. It was frustrating to be rocking the baby at 10:00 when the planner said, "Weed flower bed." So I started designing my own planner pages so that I could have a flexible plan.

Today the *Homemaker's Friend Daily Planner* is a professional version of those homemade pages of years gone by. Through twelve moves, from toddlers to adult children, to mission life in Haiti, this basic, flexible planner kept me on track while allowing me to change from one stage to the next.

WRITE WITH A PENCIL SO TASKS CAN EASILY BE ERASED AND REARRANGED.

The planner is divided into the following sections.

WEEKLY PLANNING. This user-friendly section helps you make the most out of your week and day. The "Task List" gives you a visual of what needs to be done, and you can divvy out those duties on specific days. Typically, I use a four-week menu plan, but I still write what is for dinner in the menu block.

COMPLETE THE MOST IMPORTANT TASKS FIRST FOR THE DAY OR WEEK TO BOOST PRODUCTIVITY.

MONTHLY CALENDAR. This section gives an overall view of events on the horizon. This helps me to be more realistic with weekly planning, since I can see at a glance what will be happening over the next few weeks.

YEARLY CALENDAR. This section has a place for basic notations. Now with the untitled sections, you have a place to journal or write prayer requests, birthdays, and quotes.

TASKS LIST. These pages are untitled to give you the freedom to create monthly, bimonthly, or seasonal lists.

PROJECTS AND EVENTS. This section is for occasions that need more space for writing like when planning a baby shower or a family gathering. Again, these pages are untitled for flexibility.

INFORMATION. This section can be used for phone numbers and addresses that are needed temporarily, such as an address for a card shower or the information for the eye specialist.

SHOPPING LISTS. These lists are perforated for your convenience.

I use the shopping lists several ways—sometimes as a comprehensive shopping list and other times as a central location for items needed for an upcoming event, project, or menu.

The busier I am, the more I use my planner. It helps me balance homemaking responsibilities with other obligations to create a realistic schedule. Though it is typical for me to veer from a daily plan when urgent matters arise, a written plan refreshes my memory. Mrs. Otto was right—my planner is a lifetime friend.

NEVER FORGET TO ORDER YOUR PLANNER AGAIN!

Sign up
FOR AN ANNUAL SUBSCRIPTION

Cross this task off your list once and for all. Sign up for your annual planner subscription, and you'll never need to order another planner. **Anticipate the arrival of your new planner in your mailbox each fall.**

SAVE TIME.

Sign up for an annual subscription to the *Homemaker's Friend Daily Planner*, and we will automatically send you a new planner each fall.

SAVE MONEY.

When you subscribe, you receive a $2.00 discount the first year. Each following year, you get a $1.00 discount off retail price.

Your favorite planner . . . for less.

DO IT ONCE . . . AND YOU'RE DONE.

As a subscriber, you can count on your new planner arriving each fall, year after year. You can cancel your subscription at any time.

TWO WAYS TO SIGN UP:

1. E-mail *planner@christianlight.org*

2. Call 1-800-776-0478

notes

YEARLY GOALS

_____
_____
_____
_____
_____
_____
_____
_____
_____
_____
_____
_____
_____
_____
_____
_____
_____
_____
_____
_____
_____
_____
_____
_____
_____
_____

THE SAME GOD THAT MADE A WAY
LAST TIME WILL ALSO MAKE A WAY THIS *time*.

2022 MINI CALENDARS

JANUARY

S	M	T	W	T	F	S
						1
2	3	4	5	6	7	8
9	10	11	12	13	14	15
16	17	18	19	20	21	22
23	24	25	26	27	28	29
30	31					

FEBRUARY

S	M	T	W	T	F	S
		1	2	3	4	5
6	7	8	9	10	11	12
13	14	15	16	17	18	19
20	21	22	23	24	25	26
27	28					

MARCH

S	M	T	W	T	F	S
		1	2	3	4	5
6	7	8	9	10	11	12
13	14	15	16	17	18	19
20	21	22	23	24	25	26
27	28	29	30	31		

APRIL

S	M	T	W	T	F	S
					1	2
3	4	5	6	7	8	9
10	11	12	13	14	15	16
17	18	19	20	21	22	23
24	25	26	27	28	29	30

MAY

S	M	T	W	T	F	S
1	2	3	4	5	6	7
8	9	10	11	12	13	14
15	16	17	18	19	20	21
22	23	24	25	26	27	28
29	30	31				

JUNE

S	M	T	W	T	F	S
			1	2	3	4
5	6	7	8	9	10	11
12	13	14	15	16	17	18
19	20	21	22	23	24	25
26	27	28	29	30		

JULY

S	M	T	W	T	F	S
					1	2
3	4	5	6	7	8	9
10	11	12	13	14	15	16
17	18	19	20	21	22	23
24	25	26	27	28	29	30
31						

AUGUST

S	M	T	W	T	F	S
	1	2	3	4	5	6
7	8	9	10	11	12	13
14	15	16	17	18	19	20
21	22	23	24	25	26	27
28	29	30	31			

SEPTEMBER

S	M	T	W	T	F	S
				1	2	3
4	5	6	7	8	9	10
11	12	13	14	15	16	17
18	19	20	21	22	23	24
25	26	27	28	29	30	

OCTOBER

S	M	T	W	T	F	S
						1
2	3	4	5	6	7	8
9	10	11	12	13	14	15
16	17	18	19	20	21	22
23	24	25	26	27	28	29
30	31					

NOVEMBER

S	M	T	W	T	F	S
		1	2	3	4	5
6	7	8	9	10	11	12
13	14	15	16	17	18	19
20	21	22	23	24	25	26
27	28	29	30			

DECEMBER

S	M	T	W	T	F	S
				1	2	3
4	5	6	7	8	9	10
11	12	13	14	15	16	17
18	19	20	21	22	23	24
25	26	27	28	29	30	31

2022 DATES TO REMEMBER

JANUARY

FEBRUARY

MARCH

APRIL

MAY

JUNE

JULY

AUGUST

SEPTEMBER

OCTOBER

NOVEMBER

DECEMBER

2023 MINI CALENDARS

JANUARY

S	M	T	W	T	F	S
1	2	3	4	5	6	7
8	9	10	11	12	13	14
15	16	17	18	19	20	21
22	23	24	25	26	27	28
29	30	31				

FEBRUARY

S	M	T	W	T	F	S
			1	2	3	4
5	6	7	8	9	10	11
12	13	14	15	16	17	18
19	20	21	22	23	24	25
26	27	28				

MARCH

S	M	T	W	T	F	S
			1	2	3	4
5	6	7	8	9	10	11
12	13	14	15	16	17	18
19	20	21	22	23	24	25
26	27	28	29	30	31	

APRIL

S	M	T	W	T	F	S
						1
2	3	4	5	6	7	8
9	10	11	12	13	14	15
16	17	18	19	20	21	22
23	24	25	26	27	28	29
30						

MAY

S	M	T	W	T	F	S
	1	2	3	4	5	6
7	8	9	10	11	12	13
14	15	16	17	18	19	20
21	22	23	24	25	26	27
28	29	30	31			

JUNE

S	M	T	W	T	F	S
				1	2	3
4	5	6	7	8	9	10
11	12	13	14	15	16	17
18	19	20	21	22	23	24
25	26	27	28	29	30	

JULY

S	M	T	W	T	F	S
						1
2	3	4	5	6	7	8
9	10	11	12	13	14	15
16	17	18	19	20	21	22
23	24	25	26	27	28	29
30	31					

AUGUST

S	M	T	W	T	F	S
		1	2	3	4	5
6	7	8	9	10	11	12
13	14	15	16	17	18	19
20	21	22	23	24	25	26
27	28	29	30	31		

SEPTEMBER

S	M	T	W	T	F	S
					1	2
3	4	5	6	7	8	9
10	11	12	13	14	15	16
17	18	19	20	21	22	23
24	25	26	27	28	29	30

OCTOBER

S	M	T	W	T	F	S
1	2	3	4	5	6	7
8	9	10	11	12	13	14
15	16	17	18	19	20	21
22	23	24	25	26	27	28
29	30	31				

NOVEMBER

S	M	T	W	T	F	S
			1	2	3	4
5	6	7	8	9	10	11
12	13	14	15	16	17	18
19	20	21	22	23	24	25
26	27	28	29	30		

DECEMBER

S	M	T	W	T	F	S
					1	2
3	4	5	6	7	8	9
10	11	12	13	14	15	16
17	18	19	20	21	22	23
24	25	26	27	28	29	30
31						

2023 DATES TO REMEMBER

JANUARY

_____
_____
_____
_____
_____

FEBRUARY

_____
_____
_____
_____
_____

MARCH

_____
_____
_____
_____
_____

APRIL

_____
_____
_____
_____
_____

MAY

_____
_____
_____
_____
_____

JUNE

_____
_____
_____
_____
_____

JULY

_____
_____
_____
_____
_____

AUGUST

_____
_____
_____
_____
_____

SEPTEMBER

_____
_____
_____
_____
_____

OCTOBER

_____
_____
_____
_____
_____

NOVEMBER

_____
_____
_____
_____
_____

DECEMBER

_____
_____
_____
_____
_____

PERSONALIZE THESE PAGES

FOR JOURNALING, PRAYER REQUESTS, BIRTHDAYS, ETC.

MONTHLY GOALS

_____

_____

_____

_____

_____

_____

_____

_____

_____

_____

_____

_____

_____

_____

_____

_____

_____

_____

_____

_____

_____

_____

_____

_____

THE BEST WAY IS ALWAYS *through.*
ROBERT FROST

DECEMBER

TWO THOUSAND TWENTY-ONE

notes

_____

_____

_____

_____

_____

_____

_____

_____

_____

_____

_____

_____

_____

_____

SUNDAY	MONDAY	TUESDAY
5	6	7
12	13	14
19	20	21 Winter Begins
26	27	28

NOVEMBER 21

S	M	T	W	T	F	S
	1	2	3	4	5	6
7	8	9	10	11	12	13
14	15	16	17	18	19	20
21	22	23	24	25	26	27
28	29	30				

JANUARY 22

S	M	T	W	T	F	S
						1
2	3	4	5	6	7	8
9	10	11	12	13	14	15
16	17	18	19	20	21	22
23 30	24 31	25	26	27	28	29

WEDNESDAY	THURSDAY	FRIDAY	SATURDAY
1	2	3	4
8	9	10	11
15	16	17	18
22	23	24 Christmas Eve	25 Christmas Day
29	30	31 New Year's Eve	

Cut along dotted line to expose tabs.

JANUARY

TWO THOUSAND TWENTY-TWO

notes

_____

_____

_____

_____

_____

_____

_____

_____

_____

_____

_____

_____

_____

SUNDAY	MONDAY	TUESDAY
2	3	4
9	10	11
16	17 Martin Luther King Jr. Day	18
23	24	25
30	31	

DECEMBER 21

S	M	T	W	T	F	S
			1	2	3	4
5	6	7	8	9	10	11
12	13	14	15	16	17	18
19	20	21	22	23	24	25
26	27	28	29	30	31	

FEBRUARY

S	M	T	W	T	F	S
		1	2	3	4	5
6	7	8	9	10	11	12
13	14	15	16	17	18	19
20	21	22	23	24	25	26
27	28					

WEDNESDAY	THURSDAY	FRIDAY	SATURDAY
			1 New Year's Day
5	**6**	**7**	**8**
12	**13**	**14**	**15**
19	**20**	**21**	**22**
26	**27**	**28**	**29**

Cut along dotted line to expose tabs.

FEBRUARY

TWO THOUSAND TWENTY-TWO

notes

_____

_____

_____

_____

_____

_____

_____

_____

_____

_____

_____

_____

_____

_____

SUNDAY	MONDAY	TUESDAY
		1
6	7	8
13	14 Valentine's Day	15
20	21 Presidents' Day	22
27	28	

JANUARY

S	M	T	W	T	F	S
						1
2	3	4	5	6	7	8
9	10	11	12	13	14	15
16	17	18	19	20	21	22
23 30	24 31	25	26	27	28	29

MARCH

S	M	T	W	T	F	S
		1	2	3	4	5
6	7	8	9	10	11	12
13	14	15	16	17	18	19
20	21	22	23	24	25	26
27	28	29	30	31		

WEDNESDAY	THURSDAY	FRIDAY	SATURDAY
2 Groundhog Day	3	4	5
9	10	11	12
16	17	18	19
23	24	25	26

Cut along dotted line to expose tabs.

MARCH

TWO THOUSAND TWENTY-TWO

notes

_____

_____

_____

_____

_____

_____

_____

_____

_____

_____

_____

_____

_____

_____

_____

SUNDAY	MONDAY	TUESDAY
		1
6	**7**	**8**
13 Daylight Saving Time Begins	**14**	**15**
20 Spring Begins	**21**	**22**
27	**28**	**29**

FEBRUARY	S	M	T	W	T	F	S
			1	2	3	4	5
	6	7	8	9	10	11	12
	13	14	15	16	17	18	19
	20	21	22	23	24	25	26
	27	28					

APRIL	S	M	T	W	T	F	S
						1	2
	3	4	5	6	7	8	9
	10	11	12	13	14	15	16
	17	18	19	20	21	22	23
	24	25	26	27	28	29	30

MAR

WEDNESDAY	THURSDAY	FRIDAY	SATURDAY
2 Ash Wednesday	3	4	5
9	10	11	12
16	17 St. Patrick's Day	18	19
23	24	25	26
30	31		

Cut along dotted line to expose tabs.

APRIL

TWO THOUSAND TWENTY-TWO

notes

_____
_____
_____
_____
_____
_____
_____
_____
_____
_____
_____
_____
_____
_____
_____

SUNDAY	MONDAY	TUESDAY
3	4	5
10 Palm Sunday	11	12
17 Easter	18	19
24	25	26

MARCH	S	M	T	W	T	F	S
			1	2	3	4	5
	6	7	8	9	10	11	12
	13	14	15	16	17	18	19
	20	21	22	23	24	25	26
	27	28	29	30	31		

MAY	S	M	T	W	T	F	S
	1	2	3	4	5	6	7
	8	9	10	11	12	13	14
	15	16	17	18	19	20	21
	22	23	24	25	26	27	28
	29	30	31				

WEDNESDAY	THURSDAY	FRIDAY	SATURDAY
		1	2
6	7	8	9
13	14	15 Good Friday	16
20	21	22	23
27	28	29	30

Cut along dotted line to expose tabs.

MAY

notes

SUNDAY	MONDAY	TUESDAY
1	2	3
8	9	10
Mother's Day		
15	16	17
22	23	24
29	30	31
	Memorial Day	

APRIL

S	M	T	W	T	F	S
					1	2
3	4	5	6	7	8	9
10	11	12	13	14	15	16
17	18	19	20	21	22	23
24	25	26	27	28	29	30

JUNE

S	M	T	W	T	F	S
			1	2	3	4
5	6	7	8	9	10	11
12	13	14	15	16	17	18
19	20	21	22	23	24	25
26	27	28	29	30		

WEDNESDAY	THURSDAY	FRIDAY	SATURDAY
4	5	6	7
11	12	13	14
18	19	20	21
25	26	27	28

Cut along dotted line to expose tabs.

JUNE

notes

_____

_____

_____

_____

_____

_____

_____

_____

_____

_____

_____

_____

_____

_____

SUNDAY	MONDAY	TUESDAY
5	6	7
12	13	14
19	20	21
Father's Day		Summer Begins
26	27	28

MAY						
S	M	T	W	T	F	S
1	2	3	4	5	6	7
8	9	10	11	12	13	14
15	16	17	18	19	20	21
22	23	24	25	26	27	28
29	30	31				

JULY						
S	M	T	W	T	F	S
					1	2
3	4	5	6	7	8	9
10	11	12	13	14	15	16
17	18	19	20	21	22	23
24 31	25	26	27	28	29	30

WEDNESDAY	THURSDAY	FRIDAY	SATURDAY
1	2	3	4
8	9	10	11
15	16	17	18
22	23	24	25
29	30		

JUN

Cut along dotted line to expose tabs.

JULY

notes

_____

_____

_____

_____

_____

_____

_____

_____

_____

_____

_____

_____

_____

_____

SUNDAY	MONDAY	TUESDAY
3	4 Independence Day	5
10	11	12
17	18	19
24	25	26
31		

JUNE	S	M	T	W	T	F	S
				1	2	3	4
	5	6	7	8	9	10	11
	12	13	14	15	16	17	18
	19	20	21	22	23	24	25
	26	27	28	29	30		

AUGUST	S	M	T	W	T	F	S
		1	2	3	4	5	6
	7	8	9	10	11	12	13
	14	15	16	17	18	19	20
	21	22	23	24	25	26	27
	28	29	30	31			

WEDNESDAY	THURSDAY	FRIDAY	SATURDAY
		1	2
6	7	8	9
13	14	15	16
20	21	22	23
27	28	29	30

JUL

Cut along dotted line to expose tabs.

AUGUST

TWO THOUSAND TWENTY-TWO

notes

SUNDAY	MONDAY	TUESDAY
	1	2
7	8	9
14	15	16
21	22	23
28	29	30

JULY

S	M	T	W	T	F	S
					1	2
3	4	5	6	7	8	9
10	11	12	13	14	15	16
17	18	19	20	21	22	23
24 31	25	26	27	28	29	30

SEPTEMBER

S	M	T	W	T	F	S
				1	2	3
4	5	6	7	8	9	10
11	12	13	14	15	16	17
18	19	20	21	22	23	24
25	26	27	28	29	30	

WEDNESDAY	THURSDAY	FRIDAY	SATURDAY
3	4	5	6
10	11	12	13
17	18	19	20
24	25	26	27
31			

AUG

Cut along dotted line to expose tabs.

SEPTEMBER

notes

_____

_____

_____

_____

_____

_____

_____

_____

_____

_____

_____

_____

_____

SUNDAY	MONDAY	TUESDAY
4	5	6
	Labor Day	
11	12	13
18	19	20
25	26	27

AUGUST

S	M	T	W	T	F	S
	1	2	3	4	5	6
7	8	9	10	11	12	13
14	15	16	17	18	19	20
21	22	23	24	25	26	27
28	29	30	31			

OCTOBER

S	M	T	W	T	F	S
						1
2	3	4	5	6	7	8
9	10	11	12	13	14	15
16	17	18	19	20	21	22
23 30	24 31	25	26	27	28	29

WEDNESDAY	THURSDAY	FRIDAY	SATURDAY
	1	2	3
7	8	9	10
14	15	16	17
21	22 _Autumn Begins_	23	24
28	29	30	

SEPT

OCTOBER

notes

_____

_____

_____

_____

_____

_____

_____

_____

_____

_____

_____

_____

_____

_____

SUNDAY	MONDAY	TUESDAY
2	3	4
9	10	11
	Columbus Day	
16	17	18
23	24	25
30	31	

	SEPTEMBER					
S	M	T	W	T	F	S
				1	2	3
4	5	6	7	8	9	10
11	12	13	14	15	16	17
18	19	20	21	22	23	24
25	26	27	28	29	30	

	NOVEMBER					
S	M	T	W	T	F	S
		1	2	3	4	5
6	7	8	9	10	11	12
13	14	15	16	17	18	19
20	21	22	23	24	25	26
27	28	29	30			

WEDNESDAY	THURSDAY	FRIDAY	SATURDAY
			1
5	6	7	8
12	13	14	15
19	20	21	22
26	27	28	29

OCT

NOVEMBER

notes

SUNDAY	MONDAY	TUESDAY
		1
6 Daylight Saving Time Ends	7	8
13	14	15
20	21	22
27	28	29

_____
_____
_____
_____
_____
_____
_____
_____
_____
_____
_____
_____
_____
_____

OCTOBER	S	M	T	W	T	F	S
							1
	2	3	4	5	6	7	8
	9	10	11	12	13	14	15
	16	17	18	19	20	21	22
	23 30	24 31	25	26	27	28	29

DECEMBER	S	M	T	W	T	F	S
					1	2	3
	4	5	6	7	8	9	10
	11	12	13	14	15	16	17
	18	19	20	21	22	23	24
	25	26	27	28	29	30	31

WEDNESDAY	THURSDAY	FRIDAY	SATURDAY
2	3	4	5
9	10	11 Veterans Day	12
16	17	18	19
23	24 Thanksgiving Day	25	26
30			

NOV

DECEMBER

notes

_____
_____
_____
_____
_____
_____
_____
_____
_____
_____
_____
_____
_____
_____

SUNDAY	MONDAY	TUESDAY
4	5	6
11	12	13
18	19	20
25 Christmas Day	26	27

NOVEMBER	S	M	T	W	T	F	S
			1	2	3	4	5
	6	7	8	9	10	11	12
	13	14	15	16	17	18	19
	20	21	22	23	24	25	26
	27	28	29	30			

JANUARY 23	S	M	T	W	T	F	S
	1	2	3	4	5	6	7
	8	9	10	11	12	13	14
	15	16	17	18	19	20	21
	22	23	24	25	26	27	28
	29	30	31				

WEDNESDAY	THURSDAY	FRIDAY	SATURDAY
	1	2	3
7	8	9	10
14	15	16	17
21	22	23	24
Winter Begins			Christmas Eve
28	29	30	31
			New Year's Eve

GOALS FOR JANUARY

_____

_____

_____

_____

_____

_____

SUPPLIES NEEDED/NOTES

GOALS FOR FEBRUARY

_____

_____

_____

_____

_____

_____

SUPPLIES NEEDED/NOTES

GOALS FOR MARCH

_____

_____

_____

_____

_____

_____

SUPPLIES NEEDED/NOTES

GOALS FOR APRIL

_____
_____
_____
_____
_____
_____

SUPPLIES NEEDED/NOTES

_____
_____
_____
_____

GOALS FOR MAY

_____
_____
_____
_____
_____
_____

SUPPLIES NEEDED/NOTES

_____
_____
_____
_____

GOALS FOR JUNE

_____
_____
_____
_____
_____

SUPPLIES NEEDED/NOTES

_____
_____
_____
_____

GOALS FOR JULY

_____

_____

_____

_____

_____

_____

SUPPLIES NEEDED/NOTES

GOALS FOR AUGUST

_____

_____

_____

_____

_____

_____

SUPPLIES NEEDED/NOTES

GOALS FOR SEPTEMBER

_____

_____

_____

_____

_____

_____

SUPPLIES NEEDED/NOTES

GOALS FOR OCTOBER

SUPPLIES NEEDED/NOTES

GOALS FOR NOVEMBER

SUPPLIES NEEDED/NOTES

GOALS FOR DECEMBER

SUPPLIES NEEDED/NOTES

MONTHLY RELATIONSHIP GOALS

Have you considered setting monthly goals for your personal relationships?

As homemakers, our relationships with God, our family, and friends are top priority. However, everyday tasks fill our days, and sometimes in the busyness we neglect what we value most.

Perhaps it is easier to set monthly household goals since those tasks are more obvious. We know chaos is pending if we wait to long to organize the game closet or clean the coatroom.

But monthly relationship goals provide relationship awareness even when life is busy. The special things that we do for family, friends, and strangers do make a difference. Sometimes it is in looking back that we understand that the little things we did for others were much bigger than we realized.

Monthly relationship goals help you plan to improve in the areas that need it. They can be custom-made to fit your stage of life. Your personality and circumstances will also shape them. Here are a few ideas to get you started:

AREAS OF FOCUS:	GOAL:
Relationship with God & personal growth	Read a book on prayer
Family	Have a picnic at a park
	Make banana splits
Church & community	Visit Isabella

notes

_____

_____

_____

_____

_____

_____

_____

_____

_____

_____

WEEKLY GOALS

JUST BECAUSE GOD'S PATH ISN'T ALWAYS
UNDERSTANDABLE, DOESN'T MEAN IT'S
NOT THE *right path.*

tasks list

_____   _____

_____   _____

_____   _____

_____   _____

_____   _____

_____   _____

_____   _____

_____   _____

_____   _____

INTENTIONAL CHEER _____

COME, AND LET US GO UP TO THE MOUNTAIN OF
THE LORD... HE WILL TEACH US OF HIS WAYS, AND
WE WILL WALK IN HIS PATHS... AND WE WILL WALK
IN THE NAME OF THE LORD OUR GOD FOR EVER
AND EVER. MICAH 4:2, 5

DECEMBER

29	30	1	2	3	4
5	6	7	8	9	10	11
12	13	14	15	16	17	18
19	20	21	22	23	24	25
26	27	28	29	30	31	

MONDAY 29

MENU:

TUESDAY 30

MENU:

cut here

WEDNESDAY 1

MENU:

THURSDAY 2

MENU:

FRIDAY 3

MENU:

SATURDAY 4

MENU:

SUNDAY 5

MENU:

tasks list

— Dec. 6, 2021 » Dec. 12, 2021

_____   _____
_____   _____
_____   _____
_____   _____
_____   _____
_____   _____
_____   _____
_____   _____

INTENTIONAL CHEER _____

HE WILL KEEP THE FEET OF HIS SAINTS,
AND THE WICKED SHALL BE SILENT IN DARKNESS;
FOR BY STRENGTH SHALL NO MAN PREVAIL.
I SAMUEL 2:9

DECEMBER						
			1	2	3	4
5	6	7	8	9	10	11
12	13	14	15	16	17	18
19	20	21	22	23	24	25
26	27	28	29	30	31	

MONDAY 6

_____
_____
_____
_____
_____

MENU:

TUESDAY 7

_____
_____
_____
_____
_____

MENU:

cut here

WEDNESDAY 8

MENU:

THURSDAY 9

MENU:

FRIDAY 10

MENU:

SATURDAY 11

SUNDAY 12

MENU:

MENU:

tasks list

INTENTIONAL CHEER

AND JONATHAN SAUL'S SON AROSE,
AND WENT TO DAVID INTO THE WOOD,
AND STRENGTHENED HIS HAND IN GOD.
1 SAMUEL 23:16

DECEMBER				1	2	3	4
	5	6	7	8	9	10	11
	12	13	14	15	16	17	18
	19	20	21	22	23	24	25
	26	27	28	29	30	31	

MONDAY 13

MENU:

TUESDAY 14

MENU:

cut here

WEDNESDAY 15

MENU:

THURSDAY 16

MENU:

FRIDAY 17

MENU:

SATURDAY 18

MENU:

SUNDAY 19

MENU:

tasks list

Dec. 20, 2021 » Dec. 26, 2021

INTENTIONAL CHEER

LO, THE STAR, WHICH THEY SAW IN THE EAST, WENT BEFORE THEM, TILL IT CAME AND STOOD OVER WHERE THE YOUNG CHILD WAS. WHEN THEY SAW THE STAR, THEY REJOICED WITH EXCEEDING GREAT JOY. **MATTHEW 2:9-10**

DECEMBER						
			1	2	3	4
5	6	7	8	9	10	11
12	13	14	15	16	17	18
19	20	21	22	23	24	25
26	27	28	29	30	31	

MONDAY 20

MENU:

TUESDAY 21

WINTER BEGINS

MENU:

cut here

WEDNESDAY 22

MENU:

THURSDAY 23

MENU:

FRIDAY 24

CHRISTMAS EVE

MENU:

SATURDAY 25

CHRISTMAS DAY

MENU:

SUNDAY 26

MENU:

tasks list

Dec. 27, 2021 » January 2, 2022

INTENTIONAL CHEER

THOU WILT SHEW ME THE PATH OF LIFE: IN THY
PRESENCE IS FULNESS OF JOY; AT THY RIGHT
HAND THERE ARE PLEASURES FOR EVERMORE.
PSALM 16:11

DECEMBER

				1	2	3	4
5	6	7	8	9	10	11	
12	13	14	15	16	17	18	
19	20	21	22	23	24	25	
26	27	28	29	30	31	1	
2							

MONDAY 27

MENU:

TUESDAY 28

MENU:

WEDNESDAY 29

MENU:

THURSDAY 30

MENU:

FRIDAY 31

NEW YEAR'S EVE

MENU:

SATURDAY 1

NEW YEAR'S DAY

MENU:

SUNDAY 2

MENU:

tasks list

January 3 » January 9

INTENTIONAL CHEER

AND THINE EARS SHALL HEAR A WORD BEHIND
THEE, SAYING, THIS IS THE WAY, WALK YE IN
IT, WHEN YE TURN TO THE RIGHT HAND, AND
WHEN YE TURN TO THE LEFT.
ISAIAH 30:21

JANUARY

						1
2	3	4	5	6	7	8
9	10	11	12	13	14	15
16	17	18	19	20	21	22
23	24	25	26	27	28	29
30	31					

MONDAY 3

MENU:

TUESDAY 4

MENU:

WEDNESDAY 5

MENU:

THURSDAY 6

MENU:

FRIDAY 7

MENU:

SATURDAY 8

MENU:

SUNDAY 9

MENU:

tasks list

WEEK: 2

January 10 × January 16

INTENTIONAL CHEER

AND HE SAID, BLESSED BE THE LORD GOD
OF MY MASTER ABRAHAM... I BEING IN THE WAY,
THE LORD LED ME TO THE HOUSE OF MY MASTER'S
BRETHREN.
GENESIS 24:27

JANUARY

						1
2	3	4	5	6	7	8
9	10	11	12	13	14	15
16	17	18	19	20	21	22
23	24	25	26	27	28	29
30	31					

MONDAY 10

MENU:

TUESDAY 11

MENU:

cut here

WEDNESDAY 12

MENU:

THURSDAY 13

MENU:

FRIDAY 14

MENU:

SATURDAY 15

MENU:

SUNDAY 16

MENU:

tasks list

_____   _____
_____   _____
_____   _____
_____   _____
_____   _____
_____   _____
_____   _____
_____   _____

INTENTIONAL CHEER _____

BEHOLD, THE LORD GOD WILL COME WITH STRONG
HAND... HE SHALL FEED HIS FLOCK LIKE A
SHEPHERD: HE SHALL GATHER THE LAMBS WITH HIS
ARM, AND CARRY THEM IN HIS BOSOM, AND SHALL
GENTLY LEAD THOSE THAT ARE WITH YOUNG.
ISAIAH 40:10, 11

JANUARY						1
2	3	4	5	6	7	8
9	10	11	12	13	14	15
16	17	18	19	20	21	22
23	24	25	26	27	28	29
30	31					

MONDAY 17

MARTIN LUTHER KING JR. DAY

MENU :

TUESDAY 18

MENU :

WEDNESDAY 19

MENU:

THURSDAY 20

MENU:

FRIDAY 21

MENU:

SATURDAY 22

MENU:

SUNDAY 23

MENU:

cut here

tasks list

January 24 » January 30

_____   _____
_____   _____
_____   _____
_____   _____
_____   _____
_____   _____
_____   _____
_____   _____
_____   _____
_____   _____

INTENTIONAL CHEER _____

AND WHO IS HE THAT WILL HARM YOU,
IF YE BE FOLLOWERS OF THAT
WHICH IS GOOD?
I PETER 3:13

JANUARY

						1
2	3	4	5	6	7	8
9	10	11	12	13	14	15
16	17	18	19	20	21	22
23	24	25	26	27	28	29
30	31					

MONDAY 24

MENU :

TUESDAY 25

MENU :

cut here

WEDNESDAY 26

MENU:

THURSDAY 27

MENU:

FRIDAY 28

MENU:

SATURDAY 29

MENU:

SUNDAY 30

MENU:

tasks list

January 31 » February 6

_____

INTENTIONAL CHEER

MAN'S GOINGS ARE OF THE LORD;
HOW CAN A MAN THEN UNDERSTAND
HIS OWN WAY?
PROVERBS 20:24

FEBRUARY

31	1	2	3	4	5
6	7	8	9	10	11	12
13	14	15	16	17	18	19
20	21	22	23	24	25	26
27	28					

MONDAY 31

MENU:

TUESDAY 1

MENU:

cut here

WEDNESDAY 2

GROUNDHOG DAY

MENU:

THURSDAY 3

MENU:

FRIDAY 4

MENU:

SATURDAY 5

MENU:

SUNDAY 6

MENU:

tasks list

February 7 » February 13

_____
_____
_____
_____
_____
_____
_____
_____

INTENTIONAL CHEER _____

NEVERTHELESS I AM CONTINUALLY WITH THEE:
THOU HAST HOLDEN ME BY MY RIGHT HAND.
THOU SHALT GUIDE ME WITH THY COUNSEL,
AND AFTERWARD RECEIVE ME TO GLORY.
PSALM 73:23, 24

			1	2	3	4	5
FEBRUARY	6	7	8	9	10	11	12
	13	14	15	16	17	18	19
	20	21	22	23	24	25	26
	27	28					

MONDAY 7

MENU :

TUESDAY 8

MENU :

cut here

WEDNESDAY 9

MENU:

THURSDAY 10

MENU:

FRIDAY 11

MENU:

SATURDAY 12

MENU:

SUNDAY 13

MENU:

tasks list

February 14 » February 20

_____

INTENTIONAL CHEER _____

BE STRONG AND OF A GOOD COURAGE, FEAR NOT,
NOR BE AFRAID OF THEM: FOR THE LORD THY GOD,
HE IT IS THAT DOTH GO WITH THEE; HE WILL NOT
FAIL THEE, NOR FORSAKE THEE.
DEUTERONOMY 31:6

FEBRUARY						
		1	2	3	4	5
6	7	8	9	10	11	12
13	14	15	16	17	18	19
20	21	22	23	24	25	26
27	28					

MONDAY 14

VALENTINE'S DAY

MENU:

TUESDAY 15

MENU:

WEDNESDAY 16

MENU:

THURSDAY 17

MENU:

FRIDAY 18

MENU:

SATURDAY 19

MENU:

SUNDAY 20

MENU:

tasks list

WEEK: 8

February 21 » February 27

INTENTIONAL CHEER

THEY SHALL NOT HUNGER NOR THIRST; NEITHER
SHALL THE HEAT NOR SUN SMITE THEM: FOR HE
THAT HATH MERCY ON THEM SHALL LEAD THEM, EVEN
BY THE SPRINGS OF WATER SHALL HE GUIDE THEM.
ISAIAH 49:10

FEBRUARY

		1	2	3	4	5
6	7	8	9	10	11	12
13	14	15	16	17	18	19
20	21	22	23	24	25	26
27	28					

MONDAY 21

PRESIDENTS' DAY

MENU:

TUESDAY 22

MENU:

cut here

WEDNESDAY 23

MENU:

THURSDAY 24

MENU:

FRIDAY 25

MENU:

SATURDAY 26

MENU:

SUNDAY 27

MENU:

tasks list

February 28 » March 6

_____   _____
_____   _____
_____   _____
_____   _____
_____   _____
_____   _____
_____   _____
_____   _____
_____   _____

INTENTIONAL CHEER _____

NOW THEREFORE BE NOT GRIEVED, NOR ANGRY
WITH YOURSELVES, THAT YE SOLD ME HITHER: FOR
GOD DID SEND ME BEFORE YOU TO PRESERVE LIFE.
AND GOD SENT ME BEFORE YOU TO PRESERVE YOU
A POSTERITY IN THE EARTH, AND TO SAVE YOUR
LIVES BY A GREAT DELIVERANCE. GENESIS 45:5-7

MARCH

28	1	2	3	4	5
6	7	8	9	10	11	12
13	14	15	16	17	18	19
20	21	22	23	24	25	26
27	28	29	30	31		

MONDAY 28

MENU :

TUESDAY 1

MENU :

WEDNESDAY 2

ASH WEDNESDAY

MENU:

THURSDAY 3

MENU:

FRIDAY 4

MENU:

SATURDAY 5

MENU:

SUNDAY 6

MENU:

tasks list

March 7 » March 13

INTENTIONAL CHEER

TEACH ME THY WAY, O LORD,
AND LEAD ME IN A PLAIN PATH.
PSALM 27:11

MARCH						
		1	2	3	4	5
6	7	8	9	10	11	12
13	14	15	16	17	18	19
20	21	22	23	24	25	26
27	28	29	30	31		

MONDAY 7

MENU:

TUESDAY 8

MENU:

cut here

WEDNESDAY 9

MENU:

THURSDAY 10

MENU:

FRIDAY 11

MENU:

SATURDAY 12

MENU:

SUNDAY 13

DAYLIGHT SAVING TIME BEGINS

MENU:

tasks list

March 14 » March 20

_____ _____
_____ _____
_____ _____
_____ _____
_____ _____
_____ _____
_____ _____
_____ _____
_____ _____

INTENTIONAL CHEER _____

AND MOSES SAID UNTO THE LORD, O MY LORD, I AM
NOT ELOQUENT... BUT I AM SLOW OF SPEECH, AND
OF A SLOW TONGUE. AND THE LORD SAID UNTO HIM,
WHO HATH MADE MAN'S MOUTH... NOW THEREFORE
GO, AND I WILL BE WITH THY MOUTH, AND TEACH
THEE WHAT THOU SHALT SAY. EXODUS 4:10-12

MARCH						
	1	2	3	4	5	
6	7	8	9	10	11	12
13	14	15	16	17	18	19
20	21	22	23	24	25	26
27	28	29	30	31		

MONDAY 14

MENU:

TUESDAY 15

MENU:

WEDNESDAY 16

MENU:

THURSDAY 17

ST. PATRICK'S DAY

MENU:

FRIDAY 18

MENU:

SATURDAY 19

MENU:

SUNDAY 20

SPRING BEGINS

MENU:

cut here

tasks list

March 21 » March 27

_____   _____
_____   _____
_____   _____
_____   _____
_____   _____
_____   _____
_____   _____
_____   _____

INTENTIONAL CHEER _____

IN ALL THY WAYS ACKNOWLEDGE HIM,
AND HE SHALL DIRECT THY PATHS.
PROVERBS 3:6

MARCH					
	1	2	3	4	5
6	7	8	9	10	11	12
13	14	15	16	17	18	19
20	21	22	23	24	25	26
27	28	29	30	31		

MONDAY 21

MENU :

TUESDAY 22

MENU :

cut here

WEDNESDAY 23

MENU:

THURSDAY 24

MENU:

FRIDAY 25

MENU:

SATURDAY 26

SUNDAY 27

MENU:

MENU:

tasks list

March 28 » April 3

INTENTIONAL CHEER

FEAR THOU NOT; FOR I AM WITH THEE: BE NOT
DISMAYED; FOR I AM THY GOD: I WILL STRENGTHEN
THEE; YEA, I WILL HELP THEE; YEA, I WILL UPHOLD
THEE WITH THE RIGHT HAND OF MY RIGHTEOUSNESS.
ISAIAH 41:10

MARCH						
		1	2	3	4	5
6	7	8	9	10	11	12
13	14	15	16	17	18	19
20	21	22	23	24	25	26
27	28	29	30	31	1	2
3						

MONDAY 28

MENU:

TUESDAY 29

MENU:

cut here

WEDNESDAY 30

MENU:

THURSDAY 31

MENU:

FRIDAY 1

MENU:

SATURDAY 2

MENU:

SUNDAY 3

MENU:

tasks list

April 4 » April 10

_____
_____
_____
_____
_____
_____
_____
_____
_____
_____

INTENTIONAL CHEER _____

FOR THOU ART THE GOD OF MY STRENGTH:
O SEND OUT THY LIGHT AND THY TRUTH: LET THEM
LEAD ME; LET THEM BRING ME UNTO THY HOLY
HILL, AND TO THY TABERNACLES.
PSALM 43:2, 3

APRIL						1	2
	3	4	5	6	7	8	9
	10	11	12	13	14	15	16
	17	18	19	20	21	22	23
	24	25	26	27	28	29	30

MONDAY 4

MENU:

TUESDAY 5

MENU:

WEDNESDAY 6

MENU:

THURSDAY 7

MENU:

FRIDAY 8

MENU:

SATURDAY 9

MENU:

SUNDAY 10

PALM SUNDAY

MENU:

tasks list

April 11 » April 17

_____   _____
_____   _____
_____   _____
_____   _____
_____   _____
_____   _____
_____   _____
_____   _____
_____   _____

INTENTIONAL CHEER _____

FATHER, IF THOU BE WILLING, REMOVE THIS CUP
FROM ME: NEVERTHELESS NOT MY WILL, BUT THINE,
BE DONE. AND THERE APPEARED AN ANGEL UNTO
HIM FROM HEAVEN, STRENGTHENING HIM. AND
BEING IN AN AGONY HE PRAYED MORE EARNESTLY.
LUKE 22:42-44

APRIL

					1	2
3	4	5	6	7	8	9
10	11	12	13	14	15	16
17	18	19	20	21	22	23
24	25	26	27	28	29	30

MONDAY 11

_____
_____
_____
_____
_____   MENU:
_____
_____

TUESDAY 12

_____
_____
_____
_____
_____   MENU:
_____

cut here

WEDNESDAY 13

MENU:

THURSDAY 14

MENU:

FRIDAY 15

GOOD FRIDAY

MENU:

SATURDAY 16

MENU:

SUNDAY 17

EASTER

MENU:

tasks list

April 18 » April 24

_____ _____
_____ _____
_____ _____
_____ _____
_____ _____
_____ _____
_____ _____
_____ _____

INTENTIONAL CHEER _____

AND MOSES SAID UNTO THE PEOPLE, FEAR YE NOT,
STAND STILL, AND SEE THE SALVATION OF THE LORD,
WHICH HE WILL SHEW TO YOU TO DAY: FOR THE
EGYPTIANS WHOM YE HAVE SEEN TO DAY, YE SHALL SEE
THEM AGAIN NO MORE FOR EVER. THE LORD SHALL FIGHT
FOR YOU, AND YE SHALL HOLD YOUR PEACE.
EXODUS 14:13-14

APRIL

					1	2
3	4	5	6	7	8	9
10	11	12	13	14	15	16
17	18	19	20	21	22	23
24	25	26	27	28	29	30

MONDAY 18

MENU:

TUESDAY 19

MENU:

WEDNESDAY 20

MENU:

THURSDAY 21

MENU:

FRIDAY 22

MENU:

SATURDAY 23

MENU:

SUNDAY 24

MENU:

tasks list

April 25 » May 1

_____
_____
_____
_____
_____
_____
_____
_____

INTENTIONAL CHEER _____

SIT STILL, MY DAUGHTER,
UNTIL THOU KNOW HOW
THE MATTER WILL FALL.
RUTH 3:18

APRIL

					1	2
3	4	5	6	7	8	9
10	11	12	13	14	15	16
17	18	19	20	21	22	23
24	25	26	27	28	29	30
1						

MONDAY 25

MENU:

TUESDAY 26

MENU:

WEDNESDAY 27

MENU :

THURSDAY 28

MENU :

FRIDAY 29

MENU :

SATURDAY 30

SUNDAY 1

MENU :

MENU :

tasks list

May 2 » May 8

_____

INTENTIONAL CHEER _____

EVERY WISE WOMAN BUILDETH HER HOUSE:
BUT THE FOOLISH PLUCKETH IT DOWN WITH
HER HANDS.
PROVERBS 14:1

MAY

1	2	3	4	5	6	7
8	9	10	11	12	13	14
15	16	17	18	19	20	21
22	23	24	25	26	27	28
29	30	31				

MONDAY 2

MENU:

TUESDAY 3

MENU:

cut here

WEDNESDAY 4

MENU:

THURSDAY 5

M F N U :

FRIDAY 6

MENU:

SATURDAY 7

SUNDAY 8

MOTHER'S DAY

MENU:

MENU:

tasks list

May 9 » May 15

_____

INTENTIONAL CHEER _____

I HAVE SET BEFORE THEE AN OPEN DOOR, AND
NO MAN CAN SHUT IT: FOR THOU HAST A LITTLE
STRENGTH, AND HAST KEPT MY WORD, AND HAST
NOT DENIED MY NAME.
REVELATION 3:8

MAY						
1	2	3	4	5	6	7
8	9	10	11	12	13	14
15	16	17	18	19	20	21
22	23	24	25	26	27	28
29	30	31				

MONDAY 9

MENU :

TUESDAY 10

MENU :

cut here

WEDNESDAY 11

MENU:

THURSDAY 12

MENU:

FRIDAY 13

MENU:

SATURDAY 14

MENU:

SUNDAY 15

MENU:

tasks list

May 16 » May 22

_____ _____
_____ _____
_____ _____
_____ _____
_____ _____
_____ _____
_____ _____
_____ _____
_____ _____

INTENTIONAL CHEER _____

COMMIT THY WAY UNTO THE LORD;
TRUST ALSO IN HIM;
AND HE SHALL BRING IT TO PASS.
PSALM 37:5

MAY	1	2	3	4	5	6	7
	8	9	10	11	12	13	14
	15	16	17	18	19	20	21
	22	23	24	25	26	27	28
	29	30	31				

MONDAY 16

MENU :

TUESDAY 17

MENU :

cut here

WEDNESDAY 18

MENU:

THURSDAY 19

MENU:

FRIDAY 20

MENU:

SATURDAY 21

MENU:

SUNDAY 22

MENU:

tasks list

May 23 » May 29

_____

INTENTIONAL CHEER _____

FOR THOU ART MY ROCK AND MY FORTRESS;
THEREFORE FOR THY NAME'S SAKE LEAD ME,
AND GUIDE ME.
PSALM 31:3

MAY	1	2	3	4	5	6	7
	8	9	10	11	12	13	14
	15	16	17	18	19	20	21
	22	23	24	25	26	27	28
	29	30	31				

MONDAY 23

MENU:

TUESDAY 24

MENU:

WEDNESDAY 25

MENU:

THURSDAY 26

MENU:

FRIDAY 27

MENU:

SATURDAY 28

SUNDAY 29

MENU:

MENU:

tasks list

May 30 » June 5

INTENTIONAL CHEER

I WILL INSTRUCT THEE AND TEACH THEE
IN THE WAY WHICH THOU SHALT GO:
I WILL GUIDE THEE WITH MINE EYE.
PSALM 32:8

JUNE

30	31	1	2	3	4
5	6	7	8	9	10	11
12	13	14	15	16	17	18
19	20	21	22	23	24	25
26	27	28	29	30		

MONDAY 30

MEMORIAL DAY

MENU:

TUESDAY 31

MENU:

WEDNESDAY 1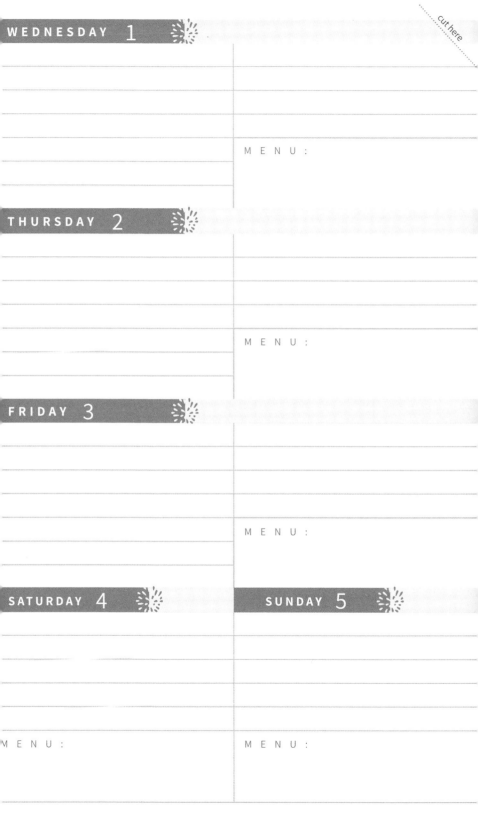

MENU:

THURSDAY 2

MENU:

FRIDAY 3

MENU:

SATURDAY 4

MENU:

SUNDAY 5

MENU:

tasks list

June 6 » June 12

INTENTIONAL CHEER

FOR I KNOW THE THOUGHTS THAT I THINK TOWARD
YOU, SAITH THE LORD, THOUGHTS OF PEACE, AND
NOT OF EVIL, TO GIVE YOU AN EXPECTED END. THEN
SHALL YE CALL UPON ME... AND YE SHALL SEEK ME,
AND FIND ME, WHEN YE SHALL SEARCH FOR ME WITH
ALL YOUR HEART. JEREMIAH 29:11-13

JUNE

			1	2	3	4
5	6	7	8	9	10	11
12	13	14	15	16	17	18
19	20	21	22	23	24	25
26	27	28	29	30		

MONDAY 6

MENU :

TUESDAY 7

MENU :

cut here

WEDNESDAY 8

MENU:

THURSDAY 9

MENU:

FRIDAY 10

MENU:

SATURDAY 11

SUNDAY 12

MENU:

MENU:

tasks list

June 13 » June 19

_____
_____
_____
_____
_____
_____
_____
_____
_____
_____
_____
_____
_____
_____

INTENTIONAL CHEER _____

A FAITHFUL MAN SHALL ABOUND
WITH BLESSINGS.
PROVERBS 28:20

JUNE

				1	2	3	4
5	6	7	8	9	10	11
12	13	14	15	16	17	18
19	20	21	22	23	24	25
26	27	28	29	30

MONDAY 13

MENU :

TUESDAY 14

MENU :

WEDNESDAY 15

MENU:

THURSDAY 16

MENU:

FRIDAY 17

MENU:

SATURDAY 18

MENU:

SUNDAY 19

FATHER'S DAY

MENU:

tasks list

June 20 » June 26

_____

_____

_____

_____

_____

_____

_____

_____

_____

INTENTIONAL CHEER

THEN JOB ANSWERED THE LORD, AND SAID, I KNOW
THAT THOU CANST DO EVERY THING, AND THAT NO
THOUGHT CAN BE WITHHOLDEN FROM THEE.
JOB 42:1-2

JUNE

			1	2	3	4
5	6	7	8	9	10	11
12	13	14	15	16	17	18
19	20	21	22	23	24	25
26	27	28	29	30		

MONDAY 20

MENU:

TUESDAY 21

SUMMER BEGINS

MENU:

cut here

WEDNESDAY 22

MENU:

THURSDAY 23

MENU:

FRIDAY 24

MENU:

SATURDAY 25

MENU:

SUNDAY 26

MENU:

tasks list

June 27 » July 3

_____   _____
_____   _____
_____   _____
_____   _____
_____   _____
_____   _____
_____   _____
_____   _____
_____   _____

INTENTIONAL CHEER _____

THE WAY OF THE JUST IS UPRIGHTNESS: THOU, MOST
UPRIGHT, DOST WEIGH THE PATH OF THE JUST. YEA,
IN THE WAY OF THY JUDGMENTS, O LORD, HAVE WE
WAITED FOR THEE; THE DESIRE OF OUR SOUL IS TO
THY NAME, AND TO THE REMEMBRANCE OF THEE.
ISAIAH 26:7-8

JUNE

			1	2	3	4
5	6	7	8	9	10	11
12	13	14	15	16	17	18
19	20	21	22	23	24	25
26	27	28	29	30	1	2
3						

MONDAY 27

MENU:

TUESDAY 28

MENU:

cut here

WEDNESDAY 29

MENU:

THURSDAY 30

MENU:

FRIDAY 1

MENU:

SATURDAY 2

MENU:

SUNDAY 3

INDEPENDENCE DAY

MENU:

tasks list

July 4 » July 10

_____
_____
_____
_____
_____
_____
_____
_____
_____

INTENTIONAL CHEER _____

FOR THOU HAST DELIVERED MY SOUL FROM
DEATH: WILT NOT THOU DELIVER MY FEET FROM
FALLING, THAT I MAY WALK BEFORE GOD IN THE
LIGHT OF THE LIVING?
PSALM 56:13

JULY

					1	2
3	4	5	6	7	8	9
10	11	12	13	14	15	16
17	18	19	20	21	22	23
24	25	26	27	28	29	30
31						

MONDAY 4

INDEPENDENCE DAY

MENU :

TUESDAY 5

MENU :

cut here

WEDNESDAY 6

MENU:

THURSDAY 7

MENU:

FRIDAY 8

MENU:

SATURDAY 9

MENU:

SUNDAY 10

MENU:

tasks list

INTENTIONAL CHEER

AND HE SAID, COME. AND WHEN PETER WAS COME
DOWN OUT OF THE SHIP, HE WALKED ON THE WATER,
TO GO TO JESUS. BUT WHEN HE SAW THE WIND
BOISTEROUS, HE WAS AFRAID; AND BEGINNING TO
SINK, HE CRIED, SAYING, LORD, SAVE ME.
MATTHEW 14:29-30

JULY						
					1	2
3	4	5	6	7	8	9
10	11	12	13	14	15	16
17	18	19	20	21	22	23
24	25	26	27	28	29	30
31						

MONDAY 11

MENU:

TUESDAY 12

MENU:

WEDNESDAY 13

MENU:

THURSDAY 14

MENU:

FRIDAY 15

MENU:

SATURDAY 16

MENU:

SUNDAY 17

MENU:

tasks list

July 18 » July 24

_____   _____

_____   _____

_____   _____

_____   _____

_____   _____

_____   _____

_____   _____

_____   _____

_____   _____

INTENTIONAL CHEER _____

AND ASA CRIED UNTO THE LORD HIS GOD, AND SAID,
LORD, IT IS NOTHING WITH THEE TO HELP, WHETHER
WITH MANY, OR WITH THEM THAT HAVE NO POWER:
HELP US, O LORD OUR GOD; FOR WE REST ON THEE,
AND IN THY NAME WE GO AGAINST THIS MULTITUDE.
O LORD, THOU ART OUR GOD; LET NOT MAN PREVAIL
AGAINST THEE. II CHRONICLES 14:11

JULY

					1	2
3	4	5	6	7	8	9
10	11	12	13	14	15	16
17	18	19	20	21	22	23
24	25	26	27	28	29	30
31						

MONDAY 18

MENU:

TUESDAY 19

MENU:

cut here

WEDNESDAY 20

MENU:

THURSDAY 21

MENU:

FRIDAY 22

MENU:

SATURDAY 23

MENU:

SUNDAY 24

MENU:

tasks list

July 25 » July 31

INTENTIONAL CHEER

HE GIVETH POWER TO THE FAINT;
AND TO THEM THAT HAVE NO MIGHT HE
INCREASETH STRENGTH.
ISAIAH 40:29

JULY

					1	2
3	4	5	6	7	8	9
10	11	12	13	14	15	16
17	18	19	20	21	22	23
24	25	26	27	28	29	30
31						

MONDAY 25

MENU:

TUESDAY 26

MENU:

cut here

WEDNESDAY 27

MENU:

THURSDAY 28

MENU:

FRIDAY 29

MENU:

SATURDAY 30

MENU:

SUNDAY 31

MENU:

tasks list

August 1 » August 7

_____   _____
_____   _____
_____   _____
_____   _____
_____   _____
_____   _____
_____   _____
_____   _____

INTENTIONAL CHEER _____

BUT THE PATH OF THE JUST IS AS
THE SHINING LIGHT, THAT SHINETH MORE AND
MORE UNTO THE PERFECT DAY.
PROVERBS 4:18

AUGUST	1	2	3	4	5	6
7	8	9	10	11	12	13
14	15	16	17	18	19	20
21	22	23	24	25	26	27
28	29	30	31			

MONDAY 1

MENU:

TUESDAY 2

MENU:

cut here

WEDNESDAY 3

MENU:

THURSDAY 4

MENU:

FRIDAY 5

MENU:

SATURDAY 6

MENU:

SUNDAY 7

MENU:

tasks list

August 8 » August 14

_____   _____
_____   _____
_____   _____
_____   _____
_____   _____
_____   _____
_____   _____
_____   _____
_____   _____

INTENTIONAL CHEER

BE STRONG AND COURAGEOUS, BE NOT AFRAID NOR DISMAYED FOR THE KING OF ASSYRIA, NOR FOR ALL THE MULTITUDE THAT IS WITH HIM: FOR THERE BE MORE WITH US THAN WITH HIM: WITH HIM IS AN ARM OF FLESH; BUT WITH US IS THE LORD OUR GOD TO HELP US. II CHRONICLES 32:7-8

AUGUST

	1	2	3	4	5	6
7	8	9	10	11	12	13
14	15	16	17	18	19	20
21	22	23	24	25	26	27
28	29	30	31			

MONDAY 8

MENU:

TUESDAY 9

MENU:

cut here

WEDNESDAY 10

MENU:

THURSDAY 11

MENU:

FRIDAY 12

MENU:

SATURDAY 13

MENU:

SUNDAY 14

MENU:

tasks list

WEEK: 33

August 15 » August 21

INTENTIONAL CHEER

BEHOLD, I AM THE LORD,
THE GOD OF ALL FLESH:
IS THERE ANY THING TOO HARD FOR ME?
JEREMIAH 32:27

AUGUST

	1	2	3	4	5	6
7	8	9	10	11	12	13
14	15	16	17	18	19	20
21	22	23	24	25	26	27
28	29	30	31			

MONDAY 15

MENU:

TUESDAY 16

MENU:

WEDNESDAY 17

MENU:

THURSDAY 18

MENU:

FRIDAY 19

MENU:

SATURDAY 20

MENU:

SUNDAY 21

MENU:

tasks list

August 22 » August 28

INTENTIONAL CHEER

THE RIGHTEOUSNESS OF THE PERFECT SHALL
DIRECT HIS WAY: BUT THE WICKED SHALL
FALL BY HIS OWN WICKEDNESS.
PROVERBS 11:5

AUGUST

	1	2	3	4	5	6
7	8	9	10	11	12	13
14	15	16	17	18	19	20
21	22	23	24	25	26	27
28	29	30	31			

MONDAY 22

MENU:

TUESDAY 23

MENU:

WEDNESDAY 24

cut here

MENU:

THURSDAY 25

MENU:

FRIDAY 26

MENU:

SATURDAY 27

MENU:

SUNDAY 28

MENU:

tasks list

August 29 » September 4

_____   _____
_____   _____
_____   _____
_____   _____
_____   _____
_____   _____
_____   _____
_____   _____
_____   _____

REMINDER:
YOUR 2023 PLANNER IS AVAILABLE. *SEE ORDER FORM IN BACK.*

INTENTIONAL CHEER

LET THINE EYES LOOK RIGHT ON, AND LET THINE
EYELIDS LOOK STRAIGHT BEFORE THEE. PONDER
THE PATH OF THY FEET, AND LET ALL THY WAYS BE
ESTABLISHED. TURN NOT TO THE RIGHT HAND NOR
TO THE LEFT: REMOVE THY FOOT FROM EVIL.
PROVERBS 4:25-27

SEPTEMBER

		29	30	31	1	2	3
4	5	6	7	8	9	10
11	12	13	14	15	16	17
18	19	20	21	22	23	24
25	26	27	28	29	30	

MONDAY 29

MENU:

TUESDAY 30

MENU:

cut here

WEDNESDAY 31

MENU :

THURSDAY 1

MENU :

FRIDAY 2

MENU :

SATURDAY 3

SUNDAY 4

MENU :

MENU :

tasks list

September 5 » September 11

_____

_____

_____

_____

_____

_____

_____

_____

_____

INTENTIONAL CHEER _____

THEN I TOLD THEM OF THE HAND OF MY GOD WHICH
WAS GOOD UPON ME; AS ALSO THE KING'S WORDS
THAT HE HAD SPOKEN UNTO ME. AND THEY SAID, LET
US RISE UP AND BUILD. SO THEY STRENGTHENED THEIR
HANDS FOR THIS GOOD WORK. NEHEMIAH 2:18

SEPTEMBER

				1	2	3
4	5	6	7	8	9	10
11	12	13	14	15	16	17
18	19	20	21	22	23	24
25	26	27	28	29	30	

MONDAY 5

LABOR DAY

MENU:

TUESDAY 6

MENU:

cut here

WEDNESDAY 7

MENU:

THURSDAY 8

MENU:

FRIDAY 9

MENU:

SATURDAY 10

MENU:

SUNDAY 11

MENU:

tasks list

September 12 » September 18

_____   _____
_____   _____
_____   _____
_____   _____
_____   _____
_____   _____
_____   _____
_____   _____
_____   _____

INTENTIONAL CHEER _____

WHEREFORE LET THEM THAT SUFFER ACCORDING
TO THE WILL OF GOD COMMIT THE KEEPING OF
THEIR SOULS TO HIM IN WELL DOING, AS UNTO A
FAITHFUL CREATOR.
I PETER 4:19

SEPTEMBER

				1	2	3
4	5	6	7	8	9	10
11	12	13	14	15	16	17
18	19	20	21	22	23	24
25	26	27	28	29	30	

MONDAY 12

MENU:

TUESDAY 13

MENU:

cut here

WEDNESDAY 14

MENU :

THURSDAY 15

MENU :

FRIDAY 16

MENU :

SATURDAY 17

MENU :

SUNDAY 18

MENU :

tasks list

September 19 » September 25

_____
_____
_____
_____
_____
_____
_____
_____
_____

INTENTIONAL CHEER _____

AND THE LORD SHALL GUIDE THEE CONTINUALLY,
AND SATISFY THY SOUL IN DROUGHT, AND MAKE FAT
THY BONES: AND THOU SHALT BE LIKE A WATERED
GARDEN, AND LIKE A SPRING OF WATER,
WHOSE WATERS FAIL NOT. ISAIAH 58:11

SEPTEMBER					1	2	3
4	5	6	7	8	9	10
11	12	13	14	15	16	17
18	19	20	21	22	23	24
25	26	27	28	29	30

MONDAY 19

_____
_____
_____
_____
_____

MENU:

_____
_____

TUESDAY 20

_____
_____
_____
_____
_____

MENU:

_____
_____

WEDNESDAY 21

MENU :

THURSDAY 22

AUTUMN BEGINS

MENU :

FRIDAY 23

MENU :

SATURDAY 24

MENU :

SUNDAY 25

MENU :

tasks list

September 26 » October 2

_____
_____
_____
_____
_____
_____
_____
_____
_____
_____

INTENTIONAL CHEER _____

HE FOUND HIM IN A DESERT LAND, AND IN THE
WASTE HOWLING WILDERNESS; HE LED HIM
ABOUT, HE INSTRUCTED HIM, HE KEPT HIM AS THE
APPLE OF HIS EYE.

DEUTERONOMY 32:10

SEPTEMBER						
				1	2	3
4	5	6	7	8	9	10
11	12	13	14	15	16	17
18	19	20	21	22	23	24
25	26	27	28	29	30	1
2						

MONDAY 26

MENU:

TUESDAY 27

MENU:

cut here

WEDNESDAY 28

MENU:

THURSDAY 29

MENU:

FRIDAY 30

MENU:

SATURDAY 1

MENU:

SUNDAY 2

MENU:

tasks list

_____

INTENTIONAL CHEER

AS AN EAGLE STIRRETH UP HER NEST, FLUTTERETH OVER HER YOUNG, SPREADETH ABROAD HER WINGS, TAKETH THEM, BEARETH THEM ON HER WINGS: SO THE LORD ALONE DID LEAD HIM, AND THERE WAS NO STRANGE GOD WITH HIM.
DEUTERONOMY 32:11-12

OCTOBER

						1
2	3	4	5	6	7	8
9	10	11	12	13	14	15
16	17	18	19	20	21	22
23	24	25	26	27	28	29
30	31					

MONDAY 3

MENU:

TUESDAY 4

MENU:

WEDNESDAY 5

MENU :

THURSDAY 6

MENU :

FRIDAY 7

MENU :

SATURDAY 8

MENU :

SUNDAY 9

MENU :

tasks list

October 10 » October 16

_____

INTENTIONAL CHEER

IT IS GOD THAT GIRDETH ME WITH STRENGTH,
AND MAKETH MY WAY PERFECT. HE MAKETH MY
FEET LIKE HINDS' FEET, AND SETTETH ME UPON
MY HIGH PLACES.
PSALM 18:32-33

OCTOBER							1
	2	3	4	5	6	7	8
	9	10	11	12	13	14	15
	16	17	18	19	20	21	22
	23	24	25	26	27	28	29
	30	31					

MONDAY 10

COLUMBUS DAY

MENU:

TUESDAY 11

MENU:

WEDNESDAY 12

MENU:

THURSDAY 13

MENU:

FRIDAY 14

MENU:

SATURDAY 15

MENU:

SUNDAY 16

MENU:

tasks list

October 17 » October 23

INTENTIONAL CHEER

FAITHFUL IS HE THAT CALLETH YOU,
WHO ALSO WILL DO IT.
I THESSALONIANS 5:24

OCTOBER

						1
2	3	4	5	6	7	8
9	10	11	12	13	14	15
16	17	18	19	20	21	22
23	24	25	26	27	28	29
30	31					

MONDAY 17

MENU:

TUESDAY 18

MENU:

WEDNESDAY 19

MENU:

THURSDAY 20

MENU:

FRIDAY 21

MENU:

SATURDAY 22

SUNDAY 23

MENU:

MENU:

tasks list

WEEK: 43

October 24 » October 30

INTENTIONAL CHEER

THEN MORDECAI COMMANDED TO ANSWER ESTHER, THINK NOT WITH THYSELF THAT THOU SHALT ESCAPE IN THE KING'S HOUSE... AND WHO KNOWETH WHETHER THOU ART COME TO THE KINGDOM FOR SUCH A TIME AS THIS? THEN ESTHER BADE THEM RETURN MORDECAI THIS ANSWER... I GO IN UNTO THE KING... AND IF I PERISH, I PERISH.
ESTHER 4:13-16

OCTOBER

						1
2	3	4	5	6	7	8
9	10	11	12	13	14	15
16	17	18	19	20	21	22
23	24	25	26	27	28	29
30	31					

MONDAY 24

MENU:

TUESDAY 25

MENU:

WEDNESDAY 26

MENU:

THURSDAY 27

MENU:

FRIDAY 28

MENU:

SATURDAY 29

MENU:

SUNDAY 30

MENU:

tasks list

tasks list

October 31 » November 6

INTENTIONAL CHEER

AND THE LORD DIRECT YOUR HEARTS INTO THE LOVE OF GOD, AND INTO THE PATIENT WAITING FOR CHRIST.
II THESSALONIANS 3:5

NOVEMBER

31	1	2	3	4	5
6	7	8	9	10	11	12
13	14	15	16	17	18	19
20	21	22	23	24	25	26
27	28	29	30

MONDAY 31

MENU:

TUESDAY 1

MENU:

cut here

WEDNESDAY 2

MENU:

THURSDAY 3

MENU:

FRIDAY 4

MENU:

SATURDAY 5

MENU:

SUNDAY 6

DAYLIGHT SAVING TIME ENDS

MENU:

tasks list

November 7 » November 13

_____

_____

_____

_____

_____

_____

_____

_____

_____

INTENTIONAL CHEER _____

FOR WE HAVE NO MIGHT AGAINST THIS GREAT
COMPANY THAT COMETH AGAINST US; NEITHER KNOW
WE WHAT TO DO: BUT OUR EYES ARE UPON THEE... BE
NOT AFRAID NOR DISMAYED... FOR THE BATTLE IS NOT
YOURS, BUT GOD'S. SET YOURSELVES, STAND YE STILL,
AND SEE THE SALVATION OF THE LORD WITH YOU.
2 CHRONICLES 20:12,15,17

NOVEMBER

		1	2	3	4	5
6	7	8	9	10	11	12
13	14	15	16	17	18	19
20	21	22	23	24	25	26
27	28	29	30			

MONDAY 7

MENU:

TUESDAY 8

MENU:

cut here

WEDNESDAY 9

MENU:

THURSDAY 10

MENU:

FRIDAY 11

VETERANS DAY

MENU:

SATURDAY 12

SUNDAY 13

MENU:

MENU:

tasks list

INTENTIONAL CHEER

NOW WHEN DANIEL KNEW THAT THE WRITING
WAS SIGNED, HE WENT INTO HIS HOUSE; AND HIS
WINDOWS BEING OPEN IN HIS CHAMBER TOWARD
JERUSALEM, HE KNEELED UPON HIS KNEES THREE
TIMES A DAY, AND PRAYED, AND GAVE THANKS BEFORE
HIS GOD, AS HE DID AFORETIME. DANIEL 6:10

NOVEMBER

		1	2	3	4	5
6	7	8	9	10	11	12
13	14	15	16	17	18	19
20	21	22	23	24	25	26
27	28	29	30			

MONDAY 14

MENU:

TUESDAY 15

MENU:

cut here

WEDNESDAY 16

MENU:

THURSDAY 17

MENU:

FRIDAY 18

MENU:

SATURDAY 19

MENU:

SUNDAY 20

MENU:

tasks list

WEEK: 47

November 21 » November 27

INTENTIONAL CHEER

ENTER INTO HIS GATES WITH THANKSGIVING,
AND INTO HIS COURTS WITH PRAISE:
BE THANKFUL UNTO HIM, AND BLESS HIS NAME.
PSALM 100:4

NOVEMBER

		1	2	3	4	5
6	7	8	9	10	11	12
13	14	15	16	17	18	19
20	21	22	23	24	25	26
27	28	29	30			

MONDAY 21

MENU:

TUESDAY 22

MENU:

WEDNESDAY 23

MENU:

THURSDAY 24

THANKSGIVING DAY

MENU:

FRIDAY 25

MENU:

SATURDAY 26

MENU:

SUNDAY 27

MENU:

tasks list

WEEK: 48

November 28 » December 4

INTENTIONAL CHEER

THEN SAID DAVID TO THE PHILISTINE, THOU COMEST
TO ME WITH A SWORD, AND WITH A SPEAR, AND WITH
A SHIELD: BUT I COME TO THEE IN THE NAME OF
THE LORD OF HOSTS, THE GOD OF THE ARMIES OF
ISRAEL, WHOM THOU HAST DEFIED.
1 SAMUEL 17:45

DECEMBER

28	29	30	1	2	3
4	5	6	7	8	9	10
11	12	13	14	15	16	17
18	19	20	21	22	23	24
25	26	27	28	29	30	31

MONDAY 28

MENU:

TUESDAY 29

MENU:

cut here

WEDNESDAY 30

MENU:

THURSDAY 1

MENU:

FRIDAY 2

MENU:

SATURDAY 3

MENU:

SUNDAY 4

MENU:

tasks list

December 5 » December 11

_____
_____
_____
_____
_____
_____
_____
_____

INTENTIONAL CHEER _____

SHEW ME THY WAYS, O LORD; TEACH ME THY
PATHS. LEAD ME IN THY TRUTH, AND TEACH ME:
FOR THOU ART THE GOD OF MY SALVATION; ON
THEE DO I WAIT ALL THE DAY.
PSALM 25:4, 5

DECEMBER					1	2	3
	4	5	6	7	8	9	10
	11	12	13	14	15	16	17
	18	19	20	21	22	23	24
	25	26	27	28	29	30	31

MONDAY 5

_____
_____
_____
_____

MENU:

TUESDAY 6

_____
_____
_____
_____

MENU:

WEDNESDAY 7

MENU:

THURSDAY 8

MENU:

FRIDAY 9

MENU:

SATURDAY 10

MENU:

SUNDAY 11

MENU:

tasks list

WEEK: 50

December 12 » December 18

INTENTIONAL CHEER

LET US RUN WITH PATIENCE THE RACE THAT IS SET
BEFORE US... LOOKING UNTO JESUS...
FOR CONSIDER HIM THAT ENDURED SUCH
CONTRADICTION OF SINNERS AGAINST HIMSELF,
LEST YE BE WEARIED AND FAINT IN YOUR MINDS.
HEBREWS 12:1-3

DECEMBER

					1	2	3
4	5	6	7	8	9	10
11	12	13	14	15	16	17
18	19	20	21	22	23	24
25	26	27	28	29	30	31

MONDAY 12

MENU:

TUESDAY 13

MENU:

cut here

WEDNESDAY 14

MENU:

THURSDAY 15

MENU:

FRIDAY 16

MENU:

SATURDAY 17

MENU:

SUNDAY 18

MENU:

tasks list

WEEK: **51**

December 19 » December 25

INTENTIONAL CHEER

THE SHEPHERDS SAID ONE TO ANOTHER, LET US NOW GO EVEN UNTO BETHLEHEM, AND SEE THIS THING WHICH IS COME TO PASS, WHICH THE LORD HATH MADE KNOWN UNTO US. AND THEY CAME WITH HASTE, AND FOUND MARY, AND JOSEPH, AND THE BABE LYING IN A MANGER. **LUKE 2:15-16**

DECEMBER

				1	2	3
4	5	6	7	8	9	10
11	12	13	14	15	16	17
18	19	20	21	22	23	24
25	26	27	28	29	30	31

MONDAY 19

MENU:

TUESDAY 20

MENU:

cut here

WEDNESDAY 21

WINTER BEGINS

MENU:

THURSDAY 22

MENU:

FRIDAY 23

MENU:

SATURDAY 24

CHRISTMAS EVE

MENU:

SUNDAY 25

CHRISTMAS DAY

MENU:

tasks list

December 26, 2022 » Jan. 1, 2023

_____ | _____

INTENTIONAL CHEER _____

FOR HE SHALL GIVE HIS ANGELS
CHARGE OVER THEE,
TO KEEP THEE IN ALL THY WAYS.
PSALM 91:11

DECEMBER					1	2	3
	4	5	6	7	8	9	10
	11	12	13	14	15	16	17
	18	19	20	21	22	23	24
	25	26	27	28	29	30	31
	1						

MONDAY 26

MENU :

TUESDAY 27

MENU :

cut here

WEDNESDAY 28

MENU:

THURSDAY 29

MENU:

FRIDAY 30

MENU:

SATURDAY 31

NEW YEAR'S EVE

MENU:

SUNDAY 1

NEW YEAR'S DAY

MENU:

tasks list

INTENTIONAL CHEER _____

SHADRACH, MESHACH, AND ABEDNEGO, ANSWERED
AND SAID TO THE KING... OUR GOD WHOM WE SERVE
IS ABLE TO DELIVER US FROM THE BURNING FIERY
FURNACE, AND HE WILL DELIVER US OUT OF THINE
HAND, O KING. DANIEL 3:16-17

JANUARY

1	2	3	4	5	6	7
8	9	10	11	12	13	14
15	16	17	18	19	20	21
22	23	24	25	26	27	28
29	30	31				

MONDAY 2

MENU :

TUESDAY 3

MENU :

cut here

WEDNESDAY 4

MENU :

THURSDAY 5

MENU :

FRIDAY 6

MENU :

SATURDAY 7

SUNDAY 8

MENU :

MENU :

tasks list

Jan. 9, 2023 » Jan. 15, 2023

INTENTIONAL CHEER

THE STEPS OF A GOOD MAN
ARE ORDERED BY THE LORD:
AND HE DELIGHTETH IN HIS WAY.
PSALM 37:23

JANUARY						
1	2	3	4	5	6	7
8	9	10	11	12	13	14
15	16	17	18	19	20	21
22	23	24	25	26	27	28
29	30	31				

MONDAY 9

MENU:

TUESDAY 10

MENU:

cut here

WEDNESDAY 11

MENU:

THURSDAY 12

MENU:

FRIDAY 13

MENU:

SATURDAY 14

MENU:

SUNDAY 15

MENU:

notes

1

TASKS LIST

TASKS LIST

15

TASKS LIST

17

TASKS LIST

notes

1

2

PROJECTS + events

3

4

PROJECTS+events

5

6

PROJECTS *events*

9

10

PROJECTS+events

13

14

PROJECTS+events

15

16

PROJECTS + events

17

18

PROJECTS+*events*

PROJECTS+events

21

22

PROJECTS +events

23

24

PROJECTS+events

25

26

PROJECTS+events

27

28

PROJECTS+ events

29

30

PROJECTS+events

PROJECTS + events

33

34

PROJECTS+events

PROJECTS +events

37

38

PROJECTS+events

41 _____

42 _____

PROJECTS+events

45

46

notes

INFORMATION

INFORMATION

INFORMATION

INFORMATION

INFORMATION

notes

SHOPPING
list

SHOPPING
list

SHOPPING
list

SHOPPING list

SHOPPING list

SHOPPING list

SHOPPING list

SHOPPING list

SHOPPING list

SHOPPING *list*

SHOPPING *list*

SHOPPING *list*

SHOPPING *list*

SHOPPING *list*

SHOPPING *list*

SHOPPING list

SHOPPING list

SHOPPING list

SHOPPING
list

SHOPPING
list

SHOPPING
list

SHOPPING list

SHOPPING list

SHOPPING list

SHOPPING list

SHOPPING list

SHOPPING list

SHOPPING list

SHOPPING list

SHOPPING list

SHOPPING list

SHOPPING list

SHOPPING list

SHOPPING list

SHOPPING list

SHOPPING list

SHOPPING *list*

SHOPPING *list*

SHOPPING *list*

SHOPPING list

SHOPPING list

SHOPPING list

SHOPPING list

SHOPPING list

SHOPPING list

SHOPPING list

SHOPPING list

SHOPPING list

SHOPPING
list

SHOPPING
list

SHOPPING
list

SHOPPING list

SHOPPING list

SHOPPING list

SHOPPING list

SHOPPING list

SHOPPING list

SHOPPING
list

SHOPPING
list

SHOPPING
list

SHOPPING list

SHOPPING list

SHOPPING list

SHOPPING list

SHOPPING list

SHOPPING list

SHOPPING *list*

SHOPPING *list*

SHOPPING *list*

SHOPPING
list

SHOPPING
list

SHOPPING
list

SHOPPING *list*

SHOPPING *list*

SHOPPING *list*

SHOPPING
list

SHOPPING
list

SHOPPING
list

SHOPPING
list

SHOPPING
list

SHOPPING
list

SHOPPING list

SHOPPING list

SHOPPING list

SHOPPING
list

SHOPPING
list

SHOPPING
list

SHOPPING *list*

SHOPPING *list*

SHOPPING *list*

SHOPPING list

SHOPPING list

SHOPPING list

SHOPPING
list

SHOPPING
list

SHOPPING
list

SHOPPING *list*

SHOPPING *list*

SHOPPING *list*

CLOTHING SIZES

GIFT ideas

THE HAPPINESS OF YOUR LIFE DEPENDS ON
THE QUALITY OF YOUR THOUGHTS.

GIFT *ideas*

ONE OF THE HAPPIEST MOMENTS IN LIFE IS WHEN YOU HAVE
THE COURAGE TO LET GO OF WHAT YOU CANNOT CHANGE.

MASTER SHOPPING LIST

FRUIT

MEAT

BAKING

BREAKFAST

VEGETABLES

FROZEN

BAKERY

PASTA + RICE

DRINKS

MISCELLANEOUS

MASTER SHOPPING LIST

PERSONAL CARE	CLEANING	SEASONINGS	CANS + JARS
	PAPER PRODUCTS	SAUCES + CONDIMENTS	
MEDICATIONS			REFRIGERATED
ANIMALS		CHILDCARE	

CHECKLIST FOR _____

CHECKLIST FOR _____

CHECKLIST FOR _____

CHECKLIST FOR _____

CHECKLIST FOR _____

CHECKLIST FOR _____

DATE	DETAILS	DEBIT	CREDIT	BALANCE	✓

DATE	DETAILS	DEBIT		CREDIT		BALANCE		✓

LEDGER PAGES

DATE	DETAILS	DEBIT	CREDIT	BALANCE	✓

DATE	DETAILS	DEBIT	CREDIT	BALANCE	✓

ORDER FORM

To order, send this completed order form to:

CHRISTIAN LIGHT PUBLICATIONS

P.O. Box 1212 . Harrisonburg, VA 22803-1212

Phone: 1-800-776-0478 · 8:30-5:00 EST

Fax: 540-433-8896 · E-mail: planner@christianlight.org · Web: www.christianlight.org

Name _____ Date _____

Mailing Address _____ Phone _____

City _____ State _____ Zip _____

2022 Daily Planner   Qty. _____ x $15.99 ea. = _____

2023 Daily Planner   Qty. _____ x $15.99 ea. = _____

(Prices subject to change without notice)

❑ **Check here to sign up for an automatic annual subscription to this planner. Subtract $2.00 from the order subtotal. We will charge your credit card annually when shipping your new planner. You may cancel at any time.**

Order Summary

Order Subtotal _____ A

Subtract for Subscription _____ B

Add state and local taxes for VA, PA , OH • (based on A) + _____ C

Shipping
• Orders under $50.00 add $5.00
• Shipping is FREE over $50.00
+ _____ D

TOTAL of A-D _____

All Payments in US Dollars

❑ Check/Money Order   ❑ Visa

❑ MasterCard   ❑ Discover   ❑ American Express

Name on Card _____

_____ - _____ - _____ - _____

Charge Card Number

_____ _____

Exp. Date   Signature

For orders shipping outside the United States, please give us a call.

THANK YOU FOR YOUR ORDER!

THANK YOU FOR CHOOSING THE

2022
HOMEMAKER'S FRIEND
daily
PLANNER